Published by John Deed and Sean MacGarry, Thriplow, England

ISBN 978-1-8382787-0-0

Text copyright © John Deed, 2020

Illustrations copyright © Sean MacGarry, 2020

Design and artwork by Flying Pigments

www.flyingpigments.co.uk

John Deed

From a village near Cambridge, England. After a career in marketing John works on an eclectic range of subjects from writing to woodworking and a few stops in-between.
Writing "The A to Z of Country Limericks" was inspired by the enjoyment of telling stories to his children when they were growing up and is John's first foray into publishing.

Sean MacGarry

Also from a village near Cambridge, England, Sean is an architect who has also produced a wide variety of illustrations over the years, including a whole collection of colourful cartoon-like pictures. These include a series of illustrations featuring many of the numbers used to mark birthday and anniversary celebrations. He has also occasionally exhibited paintings in water colour and gouache.

- *TO A HAPPIER WORLD* -

Turn the page
to start your journey...

There was a sweet toothed teen from Angola
Twenty times a day she drank cola
Constant syrupy swilling
Meant much pulling and drilling
'Til all she had left was one molar

Continent: Africa
Capital: Luanda
Size: 1.25 million square kilometres
Population: 30.8 million
Highest point: Mount Moco 2620 metres
Official language: Portugeuse
Currency: Angolan Kwanza

There was a poor farmer from Belarus
Lucky to raise the world's largest goose
It laid huge eggs of pure gold
That were too heavy to hold
So he took them to market by moose

Continent: Europe
Capital: Minsk
Size: 207,600 square kilometres
Population: 9.4 million
Highest point: Dzyarzhynskaya Hara
346 metres
Official languages: Belarusian, Russian
Currency: Belarusian Ruble

There was a slim waitress from Cameroon
With a crescent-shaped head like the moon
Which was of no use at all
'Til at the green giant's ball
She was used by the host as a spoon

Continent: Africa
Capital: Yaoundé
Size: 475,442 square kilometres
Population: 26.5 million
Highest point: Mount Cameroon
4040 metres
Official languages: French, English
Currency: CFA Franc

There was a posh Prince from Djibouti
With a long thin nose like a flute he
Sat on a leopard skin chair
Thrust his big beak in the air
Playing tunes but looking so snooty

Continent: Africa
Capital: Djibouti
Size: 23,200 square kilometres
Population: 0.92 million
Highest point: Mousa Ali 2028 metres
Official languages: Arabic, French
Currency: Djiboutian Franc

E

There was a brave girl from Eritrea
Famed as a fearless dragon slayer
She would so proudly proclaim
That the fiercest, fiery flame
Could be doused with a hand-held sprayer

Continent: Africa
Capital: Asmara
Size: 117,600 square kilometres
Population: 6.1 million
Highest point: Emba Soira 3018 metres
Languages: Tigrinya, English,
Arabic and 7 others
Currency: Eritrean Nakfa

F

There was a busy beekeeper from France
Whose uncontrollable urge to dance
Made both his feet come alive
So he could jive on a hive
With moves he called the honeycomb prance

Continent: Europe
Capital: Paris
Size: 640,679 square kilometres
Population: 67.1 million
Highest point: Mont Blanc 4810 metres
Official language: French
Currency: Euro

There was an odd man from Guatemala
Who kept an unusual impala
It was nicknamed "Mad Michael"
Rode a green unicycle
And ate pink taramasalata

Continent: North America
Capital: Guatemala City
Size: 108,889 square kilometres
Population: 17.3 million
Highest point: Volcán Tajumulco
4220 metres
Official language: Spanish
Currency: Guatemalan Quetzal

H

There was a taxi driver from Haiti
Who, politely, was rather weighty
He ate ten burgers a day
And when hailed he had to say
"No room in my cab for you matey!"

Continent: North America
Capital: Port-au-Prince
Size: 27,750 square kilometres
Population: 11.4 million
Highest point: Pic la Selle 2680 metres
Official languages: French, Haitian Creole
Currency: Haitian Gourde

There was a history student from Israel
Who would walk to her school in chain-mail
Passing the scrap metal works
Sent all the magnets berserk
And straight up into the air she did sail

Continent: Asia
Capital: Jerusalem
Size: 20,770 square kilometres
Population: 9.3 million
Highest point: Mount Meron 1208 metres
Official language: Hebrew
Currency: Israeli New Shekel

There was a jolly lass from Jamaica
Known as a celebrity baker
Her loaves would rise to the skies
And right before people's eyes
Sprang the world's first French stick skyscraper

Continent: North America
Capital: Kingston
Size: 10,991 square kilometres
Population: 2.7 million
Highest point: Blue Mountain Peak
2256 metres
Official language: English
Currency: Jamaican Dollar

K

There was a scientist from South Korea
Who spent time in an undersea sphere
She was granted her wishes
Living with sharks and fishes
But spooked by the way they would leer

Continent: Asia
Capital: Seoul
Size: 100,363 square kilometres
Population: 51.7 million
Highest point: Halla-san on Jejudo
1950 metres
Official language: Korean
Currency: South Korean Won

L.

There was a fire-eater from Lithuania
Whose pastime was pyromania
Anything you cared to name
She would consume whilst a-flame
Can you think of something zanier?

Continent: Europe
Capital: Vilnius
Size: 65,300 square kilometres
Population: 2.8 million
Highest point: Aukštojas Hill 294 metres
Official language: Lithuanian
Currency: Euro

There was an explorer from Myanmar
Whose main aim was to travel afar
So with a huge sling in place
She launched herself into space
Past all sorts of strange planets and stars

Continent: Asia
Capital: Naypyidaw
Size: 676,578 square kilometres
Population: 53.6 million
Highest point: Hkakabo Razi
5881 metres
Official language: Burmese
Currency: Burmese Kyat

There was a sly magician from Nepal
Who sold all his old tricks on a stall
From some invisible inks
To a long chain with no links
He got rich selling nothing at all

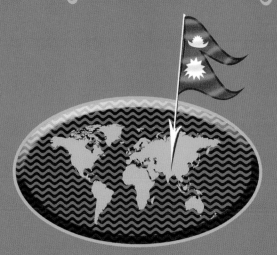

Continent: Asia
Capital: Kathmandu
Size: 147,516 square kilometres
Population: 28.1 million
Highest point: Mount Everest
8848 metres
Official language: Nepali
Currency: Nepalese Rupee

There was a storyteller from Oman
Who was able to spin a good yarn
With tales of spiders and snakes
Into the night they would take
Longer to recite than the Quran

Continent: Asia
Capital: Muscat
Size: 309,500 square kilometres
Population: 4.8 million
Highest point: Jabal Shams 3009 metres
Official language: Arabic
Currency: Omani Rial

P

There was a wicked old witch from Peru
With a recipe for fresh frog stew
With horrid warts big or small
She boiled them one and all
In a thick slimy sauce that was blue

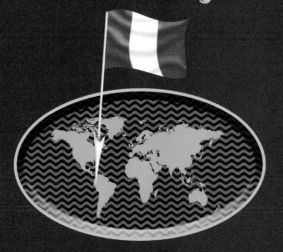

Continent: South America
Capital: Lima
Size: 1,285,216 square kilometres
Population: 32.8 million
Highest point: Huascarán 6768 metres
Official languages: Spanish, Quechua, Aymara
Currency: Peruvian Sol

There was a gifted golfer from Qatar
Also skilled at playing the guitar
He was once heard to mutter
"I've forgotten my putter"
But still finished his round under par

Continent: Asia
Capital: Doha
Size: 11,581 square kilometres
Population: 2.8 million
Highest point: Qurayn Abu al Bawl
103 metres
Official language: Arabic
Currency: Qatari Riyal

There was a shrewd scholar from Rwanda
Whose pet was a smart salamander
At mathematics it was best
And so she passed every test
Using all the help it could hand her

Continent: Africa
Capital: Kigali
Size: 26,338 square kilometres
Population: 12.4 million
Highest point: Mount Karisimbi
4507 metres
Official languages: Kinyarwanda ,
French, English, Swahili
Currency: Rwandan Franc

S

There was a bald lion tamer from Spain
But next to his big beast he felt plain
So as a matter of fact
For his sensational act
Grew whiskers and a long shaggy mane

Continent: Europe
Capital: Madrid
Size: 505,990 square kilometres
Population: 47.4 million
Highest point: Mount Teide (Tenerife)
3718 metres
Official language: Spanish
Currency: Euro

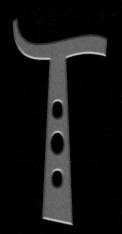

There was a trapezist from Tunisia
Whose act kept making her dizzier
Needing a boost she did cry
*6"To be able to fly high
My refreshments must be fizzier"9*

Continent: Africa
Capital: Tunis
Size: 163,610 square kilometres
Population: 11.7 million
Highest point: Jebel ech Chambi
1544 metres
Official language: Arabic
Currency: Tunisian Dinar

There was a fun-loving girl from Uganda
Who held parties on her veranda
Tigers teetering on stilts
Gorillas waltzing in kilts
And camels that dressed up as pandas

Continent: Africa
Capital: Kampala
Size: 241,038 square kilometres
Population: 42.7 million
Highest point: Mount Stanley
(Margherita Peak) 5109 metres
Official languages: English, Swahili
Currency: Ugandan Shilling

There was a show-off from Venezuela
Who became the Queen's decorator
Stately rooms in shocking paint
Caused her visitors to faint
And the King to use his inhaler

Continent: South America
Capital: Caracas
Size: 916,445 square kilometres
Population: 28.9 million
Highest point: Pico Bolívar 4978 metres
Official language: Spanish
Currency: Venezuelan Soberano

There was a flatulent fellow from Wales
Whose burps blew into force eight gales
Although he seemed such a yob
He got a lucrative job
On a millionaire's yacht filling sails

Continent: Europe
Capital: Cardiff
Size: 20,779 square kilometres
Population: 3.2 million
Highest point: Snowdon – Yr Wyddfa
1085 metres
Official languages: Welsh, English
Currency: British Pound Sterling

There was a King from a land called X-ico
Ever so vain and complex you know
He made a royal decree
"Henceforth, it's all about ME!"
Which is why it's now called Mexico

Continent: South America
Capital: Mexico City
Size: 1,972,550 square kilometres
Population: 128.7 million
Highest point: Volcán Citlaltépetl
(Pico de Orizaba) 5636 metres
Languages: Spanish and 68 others!
Currency: Mexican Peso

There was a careless gardener from Yemen
Who had sown some seeds to grow melons
With fruits yellow and shiny
They looked ever so tiny
What she'd actually grown were lemons

Continent: Asia
Capital: Sana'a
Size: 527,968 square kilometres
Population: 28.5 million
Highest point: Jabal An-Nabi Shu'ayb
3666 metres
Official language: Arabic
Currency: Yemeni Rial

Z

There was a stonemason from Zanzibar
Who constructed the world's weirdest car
It was carved out of granite
The toughest on the planet
But drove slower than a snail by far

Continent: Africa
Capital: Zanzibar City
Size: 2,462 square kilometres
Population: 1.3 million
Highest point: Masingini 119 metres
Official languages: Swahili, Arabic, English
Currency: Tanzanian Shilling

Journey's end.

Printed in Poland
by Amazon Fulfillment
Poland Sp. z o.o., Wrocław